Schott New York

Douglas J. Cuomo
b.1958

Sorry for Your Loss

for soprano and piano

Text by Lisa Rubenson

ED 30137

www.schott-music.com

Mainz · London · Madrid · New York · Paris · Prague · Tokyo · Toronto
© 2014 SCHOTT MUSIC CORPORATION, New York · Printed in USA

Performance notes:

This piece is quite conversational and while I have marked a number of pauses, ritards, accelerandos, etc., you should exercise rhythmic flexibility and a general freedom with these markings throughout the piece.

Likewise all metronome markings serve only as approximate guidelines.

The piano figure that first occurs at bar 14 and then throughout the piece indicates Christine erasing the message before she leaves it. They are generally marked *Tempo Primo*, indicating they should be approximately the same tempo as section A.

Douglas J. Cuomo
2014

Commissioned by Lyric Fest and John and Sandra Stouffer,
American Women Poets in Song, March 2014

Sorry for Your Loss

for Christine Brewer

Lisa Rubenson

Douglas J. Cuomo

© 2014 Schott Music Corporation, New York (ASCAP)

ED30137

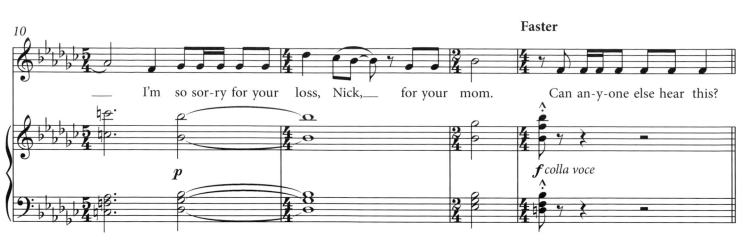

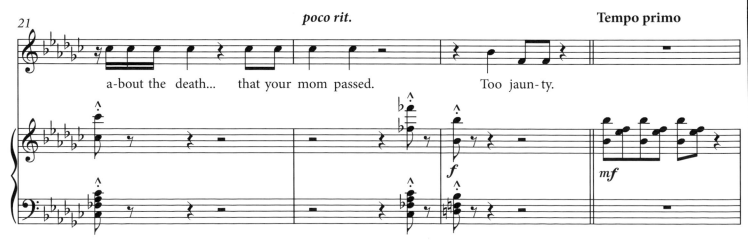

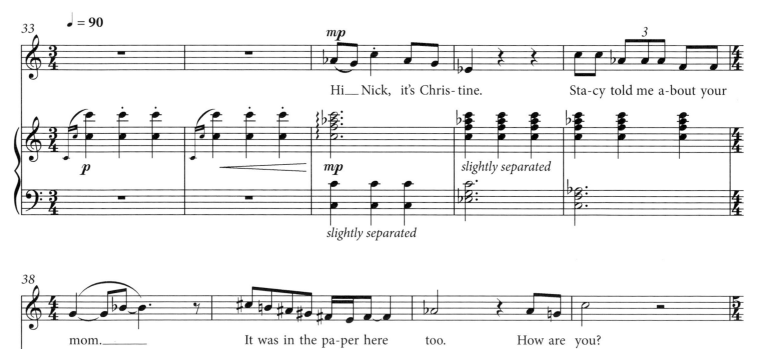

poco rit. **Slightly slower**

What a thing to say, I____ am sor - ry. For_____ ev' - ry - thing.

Your mom and I Well what-ev - er,

you know, but still I was fond of her. Is that what I was?

Tempo primo

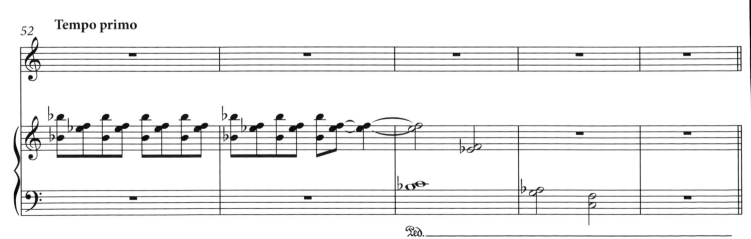

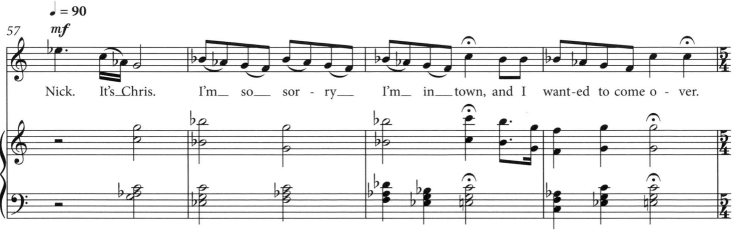

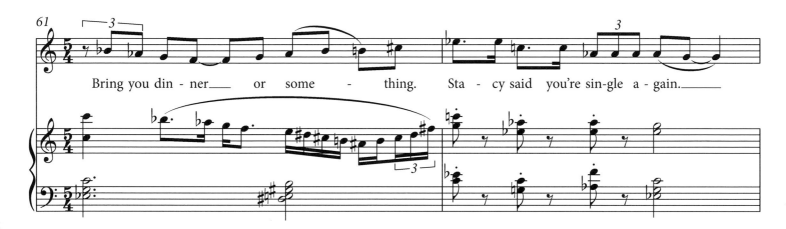

Chris-tine, it's Nick, love of your life...

Nice.

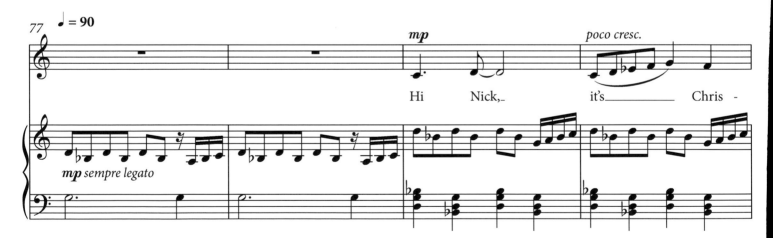

Hi Nick,_ it's_____ Chris -

tine._____ it's been so long. I'm in town. Lis-ten, I'm

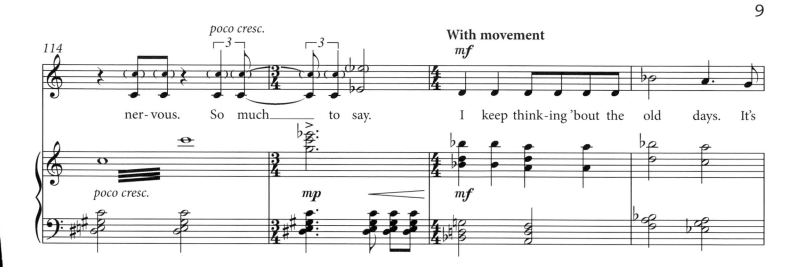

ner-vous. So much_____ to say. I keep think-ing 'bout the old days. It's

weird. I have a teen-a-ger now, a daugh - ter, the_ same age as

we_ were. I think a-bout us and it's hard._____ I think a-bout ski - ing

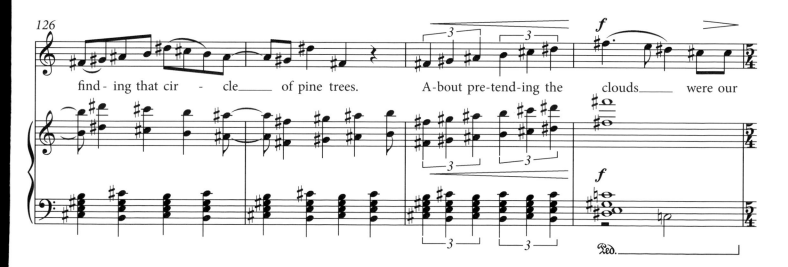

find - ing that cir - cle_____ of pine trees. A-bout pre-tend-ing the clouds_____ were our

kids and giv-ing them all Greek god names. A-bout sit-ting down for din-ner

with our fac - es bright red. Your mom thought we were

up to some-thing, but we were just burned by the sun___ and the wind___ and the

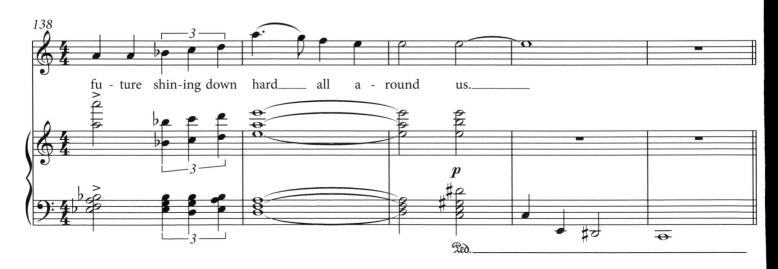

fu - ture shin-ing down hard___ all a - round us.___

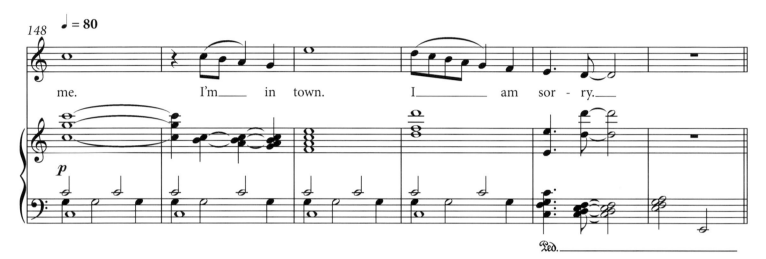

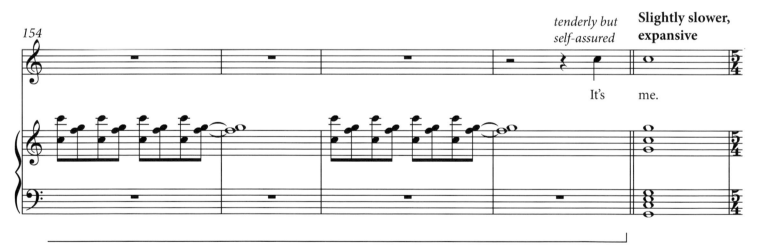